The SCIE[NCE OF] BALLOONS

BY DAVID CROFTS
ILLUSTRATED BY SANDY THORNTON

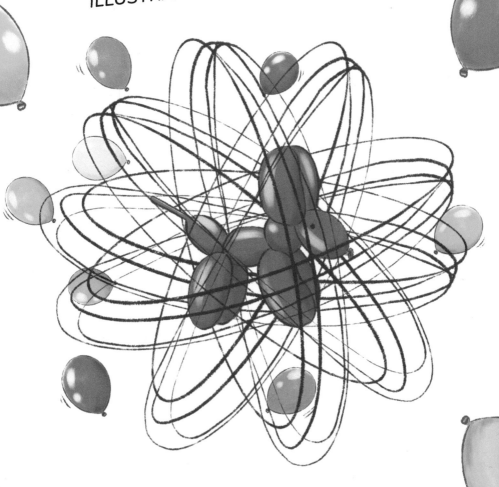

AN EXPLORATION OF SCIENCE USING MODELLING BALLOONS

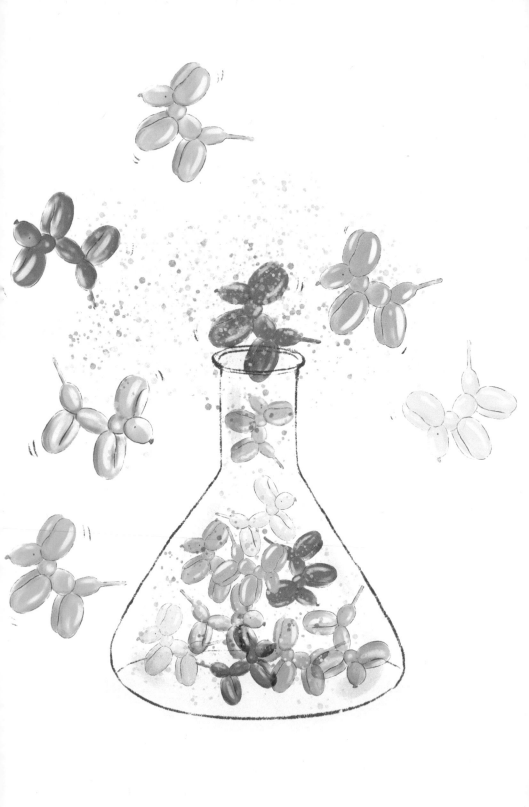

CONTENTS

THE SCIENCE OF BALLOONS
An exploration of science using modelling balloons

First published in Great Britain in 2022 by Balloon Animal

Designed by Amy Cooper

A CIP record for this title is available from the British Library

ISBN 978-1-7396081-0-1

1 3 5 7 9 10 8 6 4 2

Printed in the UK

INTRODUCTION

Rubber balloons were invented by the famous English scientist Michael Faraday in 1824. Faraday also invented the electric motor, possibly nearly as important an invention as the balloon, but he is most of all remembered for his discoveries in chemistry.

For his experiments with the gas hydrogen, he needed an expandable container which could hold the gas, and this led to the invention of the balloon, cleverly created by sticking two thin flat pieces of rubber together along the edges. When you buy balloons you will sometimes notice some very fine chalk dust in and around them which stops the rubber from sticking to itself. Faraday used flour.

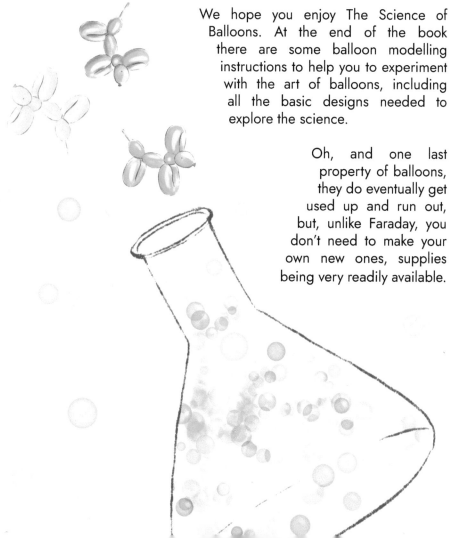

We hope you enjoy The Science of Balloons. At the end of the book there are some balloon modelling instructions to help you to experiment with the art of balloons, including all the basic designs needed to explore the science.

Oh, and one last property of balloons, they do eventually get used up and run out, but, unlike Faraday, you don't need to make your own new ones, supplies being very readily available.

Static Electricity

All things around us including balloons are made of atoms. And atoms are composed of even smaller particles called electrons, protons and neutrons. Electrons are negatively charged, protons are positively charged and neutrons are neutral, neither positive nor negative.

With a little bit of static electricity modelling balloons are very good at sticking to the wall, or the ceiling, or magically attaching themselves to somebody's back when they're not looking. Different materials have different amounts of attraction for electrons and when two materials rub against each other it is likely that one will steal electrons from the other.

If you rub a balloon against your hair, the balloon will steal negative electrons from your hair and become negatively charged. This leaves your hair positively charged. Opposite charges attract so the balloon will stick to your hair and as your hair is now positively charged, and like charges repel, your hair will stand on end. Each hair is trying to get as far away as possible from the hair next to it and in pop culture (pun intended) this has also become the classic 'mad scientist' hair style of choice.

You can now make a balloon stick to other surfaces such as a wall or ceiling. This happens because the negative charge of the balloon forces some of the electrons on the surface of the wall to move to the other side of their atoms, leaving the wall positively charged. Once again, opposite charges attract so the balloon sticks to the wall (although it's still quite ok to pretend it's magic!)

Sometimes you'll find a balloon can stick to the wall for hours on end. But moisture in the air can steal electrons back from the balloon, so on humid days, when there is moisture in the air, it might not work at all.

Centre of Gravity

A balloon dog does not always stand up very well, even with perfect proportions and the tidiest of twists. It is more likely to wobble over, lie down and go to sleep until woken up by the slightest breeze blowing it off the table. Static as explained earlier can also overpower a balloon dog's ability to behave.

In addition to the rounded shape of the feet, movement of air, and static, the Centre of Gravity is too high. If you have left the end of the tail uninflated, the heaviest part of the balloon is actually this little uninflated tail, where not being inflated the rubber is thicker. Depending on proportions it can be as heavy as the rest of the balloon put together.

So we therefore need to lower the dog's Centre of Gravity and we can do that by positioning weights at the feet. Coins work well. Once a balloon dog is made, slide in a coin where the feet would be, in between the front leg bubbles and another between the back leg bubbles. Small coins will be fine or you could create an expensive version. Now that the Centre of Gravity is very low, the heaviest part of the balloon model is at the base, and the dog stands up. If you push the dog over, it will bounce back to its feet again just like magic and if you drop it on the table from up high it will land on its feet (don't try with a real dog).

Alternatively put a coin between the front feet only and the dog will skilfully balance on its front legs with its back legs hanging over the edge of the table – an incredible feat of balance!

Strong and Weak Materials

Balloons are very strong . . . until you blow them up. Uninflated modelling balloons are difficult to snap in half by hand. It's more likely you'll be snapped by the balloon and when the ends are tied together they make strong rubber bands — nice big chunky rubber bands for general use around the home; perfect for flicking too.

However, we all know how fragile a simple balloon model can be. One little encounter with something slightly rough or sharp edged, in the home and certainly in the garden, and that's it. Balloon animals truly know why blades of grass are called blades! When balloons are inflated, they are stretched and the rubber becomes much thinner. You might even notice some of the colours getting lighter and the balloon becoming more transparent. The air is pushing against the inside of the balloon, trying to escape.

When you hear a particularly loud and sudden pop from a balloon, usually when a balloon has been overinflated with too much air, the tear across the rubber happens so fast that it actually moves faster than the speed of sound. That big boom, that makes everyone jump, is in fact a mini sonic boom, a sound normally associated with aircraft traveling faster than sound.

Balloon models made out of lots and lots of balloons can seem surprisingly robust and can be handled quite roughly but this is partly due to the fact that if a design is made with many balloons it doesn't really matter if the odd one gets popped!

So, are balloons strong or weak? We'll let you decide. You could even have a balloon debate.*

I guess it's all relative

---

* a balloon debate is the name for a type of debate where different opinions are represented by balloons and these are popped as the discussion goes along.

Friction

When twisting your designs it's best to avoid scraping and friction. Friction is the force between two surfaces which are trying to move or slide across each other and with balloons this can result in popping. Sometimes when twisting two balloons together, you can hear a squeaky scratchy sound from the friction...and this can cause damage to the thin surface of the balloon . . . and **pOp**.

When making two balloon twists close together it can be best to pull the balloon sections slightly apart as you twist. It's much more likely that the balloon would be damaged by friction than by stretching.

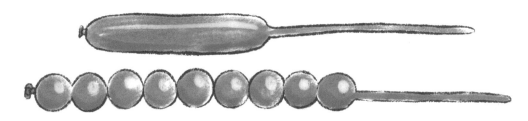

Exponsion
ond Pressure

As you twist a modelling balloon, there needs to be some uninflated balloon for the air to move along to and fill. This is one of the secrets of balloon modelling. When twisted, the volume in a given length of balloon changes because of the rounded shape of the twisted bubbles.

A certain amount of air can fit into a given length of balloon when there are no bubble shapes twisted into it, but as soon as there are bubble shapes, these shapes have curved spherical surfaces which create 'cutaways' The overall volume for the same given length of balloon is now smaller because of the cutaways. When twisted, the air has got to go somewhere so it pushes its way along expanding and filling more of the balloon.

It's no good fully inflating a modelling balloon and trying to make lots and lots of twists. This will create a steady increase in pressure and . . . **pOp**.

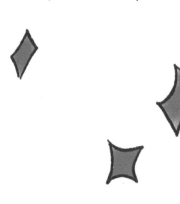

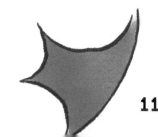

Acoustics

You can make a twangy guitar-like sound from a stretched balloon, especially if there is a small bubble inflated at the end to help to amplify the sound. The stretched balloon is like a guitar string and the air-filled bubble acts as a resonating chamber, like the wooden hollow body of a guitar, amplifying the sound.

The more the balloon is stretched, the more tension, and as with a real guitar, the higher the note will be. The less it is stretched, the lower the note will be, resulting in a sound more like a bass guitar. When the note is high, the balloon is vibrating quickly, or with a high frequency, and when the note is low the balloon is vibrating at a lower frequency.

The higher notes can be more effective and can be made to sound louder and clearer. By changing the amount of stretch while you twang the balloon it's even possible to play a song. Start with simple melodies like 'Twinkle Twinkle Little Star' or 'Happy Birthday' before embarking on a Beethoven symphony.

If you hold the end of a long, fully inflated balloon against your mouth as you speak or make a noise the sound waves will travel down the balloon. Put the other end against your ear, or someone else's ear, and the sound can be heard coming directly from the end, through the balloon, as if from a tiny, tinny speaker. The sound waves and vibrations have travelled along the balloon.

Pressure and Compression

A balloon pump is highly recommended, we would say essential. You would not try blowing up bicycle tyres by lung power alone and modelling balloons are not much easier. Balloon pumps, like bicycle pumps or football pumps, work on the principle of compression.

If air pressure is higher in one space than another, and if there is an opening between the two spaces, the air will be forced from the area of high pressure to the area of low pressure. This is also the case when the leaves on the trees are dancing or when your bundle of balloons is blown down the road on your way out of the party. The air is blowing into an area of low pressure from an area of higher pressure, in other words it's a windy day.

When the handle of the balloon pump is pulled out, air fills up the chamber. When the handle is pushed back in, the opening where the air came in closes and the pressure builds up because you are shortening the length of the tube. Air is forced out through the nozzle and into the balloon.

The openings that allow the air to move in or move out are controlled by valves. When pulling the handle out one valve opens allowing the pump to fill with air. When pushing the handle this valve closes and another valve opens, allowing the air to be forced out and into a balloon.

Some balloon pumps are simply little squeezy hollow balls with simple valves and pointed nozzles and others are sophisticated 'two-way pumps' where air is pushed out into the balloon when both pulling and pushing the handle.

Once a balloon is blown up, the air pressure inside the balloon is higher than the air pressure around us and outside the balloon, and it is this higher pressure which holds the balloon out in its blown-up shape.

Work and Heat

Hold a long modelling balloon with one hand on each end and feel the temperature of the balloon. You can do this by touching the middle of the balloon just below your nose as if sniffing it. There is nothing really to notice, neither hot nor cold, just room temperature (or rather, balloons-in-a-bag temperature).

Now stretch the balloon quickly, keep it stretched and taught as wide as you can, and feel again. It feels much hotter. Now, release the tension so that it is no longer stretched and feel once more. It will be instantly cool.

The faster you stretch the balloon, the hotter the balloon will feel. Rubber, like everything else, is made of groups of atoms called molecules and when the balloon is stretched the molecules become organised into long chains. And to do that, as the balloon is stretched, work has been done. In science, as well as in everyday life, when work is done, you sometimes notice a little bit of heat.

I'm a hot dog

Molecular Arrangement

If you take a brand new balloon, inflate it, but then forget to tie it up (I know, a bit silly), or if you let the air out by mistake, maybe when passing it to someone else to tie, this balloon can be blown up and used again . . . but it will be weaker.

Inflating the second time you might notice that the balloon blows up a little bit bigger. Being weaker, the air can push the sides of the balloon out further. The balloon itself will blow up a tiny bit wider, whereas the actual rubber will be stretched thinner.

Before being re-inflated the balloon also looks old and wrinkly, no longer brand new and pristine. Now, it can be made to, at least, look as good as new, if not be as good as new. One big stretch (that's the balloon not you), one more for luck and there we are, looks just like new . . . as if by magic.

When the balloon is new and unused, the molecules are criss-crossed all over the place in a random state. Once inflated they're straightened into long straight lines. When the air is let out some of the molecules stay lined up in chains, making it look mis-shaped and no longer new. A few of those chains will also have been broken, weakening the balloon.

When we give the balloon a quick stretch it jogs all the molecules about and helps to restore their random criss-cross arrangement. Well, we'd better remember to tie it up next time anyway.

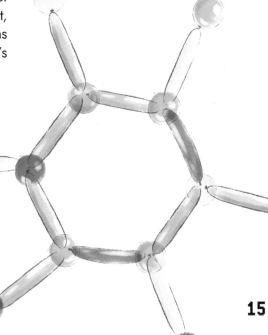

Material Memory and Elasticity

Sometimes a balloon model can be carefully unravelled, that is if you can remember which way to untwist. If you are twisting a long string of bubbles, perhaps to make a bunch of grapes or a bracelet, it's important that you keep twisting in the same direction, clockwise or anti-clockwise, otherwise some of the bubbles will start untwisting as you go along.

Once a balloon animal is finished, the curved bubbles pull together and stay positioned as close to each other as they can because of the stretchy, elastic nature of the rubber.

The elasticity of a material is its ability to return to its original size and shape after being distorted by a force.

An uninflated balloon is highly elastic and when stretched it certainly returns to its original shape. But once a modelling balloon is inflated it can sometimes be made to remember a new shape . . . and that is without being twisted.

Just bending the balloon won't really work — it will spring back again. But by folding a long balloon in half and giving it a quick squeeze it can be made to stay in position and remember its new shape. Try folding a balloon in half, squeezing at the bend, and, keeping your fingers squeezed, pulling them away quickly. This will transform the straight balloon into a 'V' shaped balloon.

The outside of the curve will be permanently stretched, the inside remaining as it was. The curve or bend is similar to a running track, where the outside of a curved track is longer than the inside.

The balloon can be thought of as having a memory. You're not giving the balloon a memory, it already has a memory and you are effectively feeding data into its memory! It's possible to make different shapes from a long balloon, lightning shaped zig-zags or even a heart shape starting with a balloon tied into a loop.

Deflation and Diffusion

Have you ever wondered how and why balloons deflate or go down slowly over time? The air is not just escaping through the knot. It's escaping through tiny invisible holes all over the surface of the balloon. The process is called diffusion and the rate of diffusion of air from a balloon depends on the speed of the molecules.

Diffusion is the movement of molecules or particles from an area of higher concentration to an area of lower concentration and the air molecules are diffusing through the sides of the balloon. The speed of the molecules depends on their temperature and their size.

The hotter the molecules, the faster they will move. Place a balloon model in the fridge or freezer and the reduced molecular speed leads to less diffusion. The balloon model will last longer.

It can be amazing how well a balloon design can hold its shape as it gradually goes down, especially if kept cool and away from direct sunlight. Try making two balloon dogs. Keep one on the window ledge and one in the fridge. The one in the fridge will stay fresh and 'dog like' for much longer than the other (again, don't try with a real dog).

It is not only hotter molecules that move faster; smaller, lighter molecules also move faster. The molecules in lighter gasses such as helium (the gas sometimes used to make balloons float) therefore move faster at any given temperature, leading to faster diffusion. That is why helium balloons loose their ability to float in just a day or so. (More about helium later).

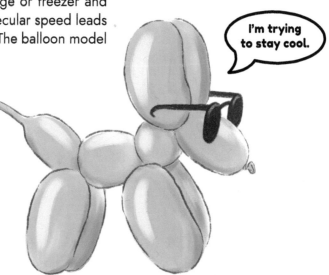

I'm trying to stay cool.

Oxidisation

Balloons are made from latex, a natural product which comes from the rubber tree, Hevea brasiliensis. Plants and animals all have Latin scientific names as well as a common name. The small 'b' is not a misprint; the Latin names consist of one name with an uppercase letter (the Genus, which is a group name) and one with lower case (the species, a more specific name).

Also just to menshion THat, this book has bee;n thouroughly proof red for eny spelling misteakes ant ovver errors, tyypos ect. But dooo kount them if yo spott @Ny and let us no

The latex is harvested, and the farmer can continue to get latex from the same trees for many years. Natural products tend to decompose or change over time and balloons are no different. Balloons start oxidising as soon as they are exposed to air and sunlight. Oxidising means mixing with oxygen and you can see the same process happening when metal starts to rust. When oxidising, balloons start to lose their shine and sheen and begin to look more dull and matte.

Fortunately, being a natural product, when a balloon model eventually reaches the end of its life and is discarded, the balloon will decompose and rot down like other vegetable matter. All rubber balloons are biodegradable, not just the green ones. However as the process is not immediate it is important to tidy up any left over or broken pieces of balloon very carefully, especially if balloon modelling outside as they could cause harm to animals of the 'real' variety.

So the rubber comes from trees, goes back into the ground and therefore eventually back into plants and trees; perfect recycling, especially if the balloon model was a flower or a palm tree to begin with!

Aerodynamics and Air Resistance

Aerodynamics is the science of how objects interact with, and move through, air. This is useful for aircraft design, balloon model bows and arrows, and flying mice (see the basics of balloon modelling).

A balloon can be made to fire straight off your finger like an arrow. Inflate a long modelling balloon, straighten it as much you can and push it onto your finger, pushing your finger into the end of the balloon, turning it round and round at the same time. This rotating action imparts a spin to the balloon along its long axis and as you release the balloon, and it flies off your finger, it will fly off with a rotating motion. The spin will improve the aerodynamics and help it to fly straighter and therefore faster and further. This is the same principle by which a bullet is made to fly in a straight line from the barrel of a rifle. The inside of the barrel is spiralled giving the bullet its spin or 'rifling effect', helping it to fly straight.

Try aiming just very slightly upwards (with the balloon, not a rifle) and with a little bit of static electricity, the balloon can be made to fly up and stick straight onto the ceiling.

Hold two balloons out side by side, one fully inflated and one uninflated, and drop them at the same time. The inflated balloon will slowly drift to the ground while the uninflated balloon will reach the ground much more quickly. Both balloons have exactly the same weight, but one has a much bigger surface area. The bigger surface area creates more air resistance, sometimes called drag, and the air resistance makes it more difficult for it to be pushed or pulled through the air.

HOME SWEET HOME

Rubber and Vulcanisation

Vulcanisation is a chemical process in which sulphur is added to rubber. The sulphur changes the molecular structure by making links between the chains of molecules. Vulcanised rubber is less sticky and much stronger. The 'curing' of rubber has been carried out since prehistoric times, but this modern process was developed in the 19th Century. It is named after Vulcan, the Roman god of fire. (It was not invented by Vulcan, the Roman god of fire, although, as well as being the god of fire and living beneath a volcano, nice, he was also an inventor).

Vulcanised rubber is used for making many things in addition to balloons, including tyres, hose pipes and the soles of shoes. Sulphur is also used in the manufacture of many other different products from skin cream to road surfaces.

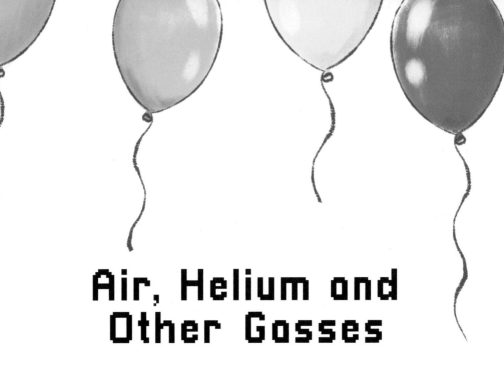

Air, Helium and Other Gasses

The air we breathe is composed of several different gases; oxygen, which is important to humans and animals, carbon dioxide, which is important to plants, and some other gases, including nitrogen, which is actually the largest component of air.

Helium is a gas which is sometimes used to make balloons float. It's the second most common element in the universe, but here on Earth it is extracted from under the ground.

Interestingly, twisted balloon animals do not tend to float very well when filled with helium. This is because of the mass to volume ratio. The mass of the rubber is too high compared to the volume of the inflated balloon. In other words, the rubber of the balloon is too heavy in comparison to the amount of helium that can fit inside the twisted balloon model.

Helium is lighter than air, so when a round balloon is filled with helium it wants to rise through the air in the same way bubbles will rise to the surface of water. With a round balloon there is less rubber in relation to the space inside, so it will float better than a balloon animal.

However, helium filled balloons do lose their ability to float in just a day or so. The helium escapes through the side of the balloons faster than air because of the smaller and faster moving molecules. Shiny metallic looking balloons allow less movement of molecules through their sides and will float for longer.

Potential and Kinetic Energy

A balloon mouse, which can be as simple as a little balloon bubble with a long tail and two eyes drawn on (a slightly more detailed version with two little ears added is described in the next section) can be fired up into the air by stretching the tail and then releasing like a catapult (should be called mouseapult). Hold the body of the mouse between your outstretched fingers so that as your other hand pulls the tail it is free to launch.

Because the empty tail is actually heavier than the main air bubble of the mouse's body, it goes up, performs a summersault and then elegantly descends tail first as if by parachute.

When the tail is stretched it becomes full of stored energy – this is called potential energy. When you let go, that potential energy is immediately converted into kinetic energy. That's the energy of motion. The more the tail is stretched, the more potential energy, and therefore the more kinetic energy and the higher and faster the mouse will go. When the energy runs out, the mouse turns round and returns to ground.

An even simpler but equally enjoyable demonstration of potential energy being transformed into kinetic energy, can be performed by blowing up a long or round balloon and just letting go (yes, without tying).

As you hold the inflated balloon, ready for blast off, it's full of potential energy, let go and the energy is turned into kinetic as the balloon sails chaotically around the room, usually complete with sound effects.

And on that note, it's time to learn the basics of balloon modelling . . .

The important bit!

THE BASICS OF BALLOON MODELLING

How to **BLOW UP** a balloon (with a pump that is, not dynamite). Next time we'll stick to the word inflate to diffuse any confusion.

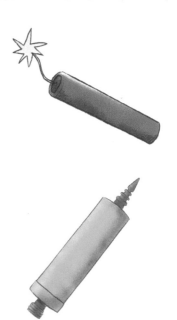

EITHER place the balloon on the end of the balloon pump and start pumping – in which case the balloon will most probably fly off across the room (very amusing, especially if it lands on someone's head)

OR carefully hold the balloon onto the end of the pump while pumping – in which case the balloon will blow up properly . . . ready for the next step . . .

How to **TIE** the balloon. To make the balloon easier to tie, release a little puff of air first. This provides an extra little length of balloon at the end for easier tying. One knot is all it takes, just like tying a knot at the end of a piece of string.

Ready for some simple shapes?

... **A WORM** (very realistic and detailed), a juggling hoop (that was easy), **throw it, spin it, cotch it** on another balloon, add some static and stick it to the wall...

... a helix, twist or tie two balloons together at their ends and then twirl them around one another...like a giant candy cane or marshmallow.

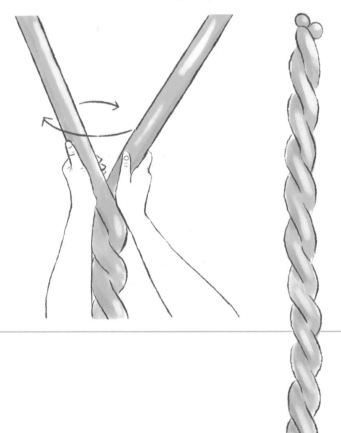

How to **TWIST** a loop.

Find the end of the balloon with the knot ...not there, try the other end,
Twist from the knotted end — the air will move further along the balloon
with each twist.

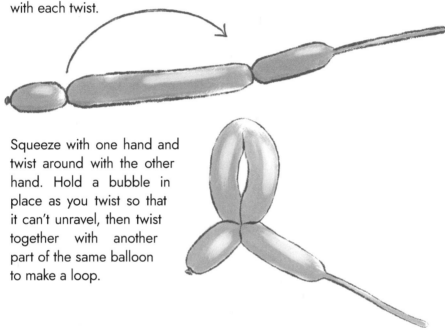

Squeeze with one hand and
twist around with the other
hand. Hold a bubble in
place as you twist so that
it can't unravel, then twist
together with another
part of the same balloon
to make a loop.

Use a **LONG BALLOON** for a sword, or a design with only
a few twists and turns, and a **SHORTER BALLOON**
(leaving some uninflated) for an animal, or a design with lots of
twists and turns.

Ready for
some proper
designs?

ONE LOOP, push the long end through

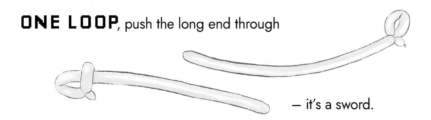

— it's a sword.

TWO LOOPS next to each other for wings, leaving some balloon left over for a body — it's a butterfly.

Turn the design the other way round — a hummingbird with a long beak.

Two tiny loops for ears, and not much air in the balloon — it's a mouse with a long tail.

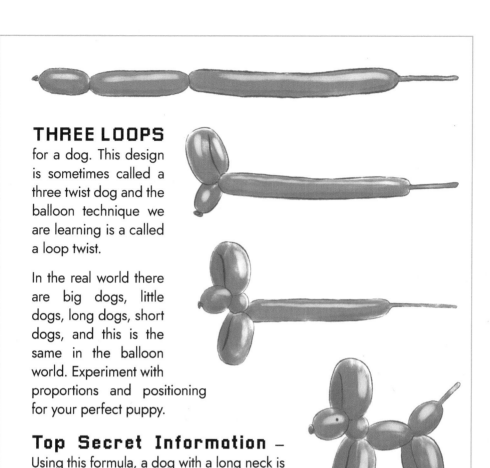

THREE LOOPS

for a dog. This design is sometimes called a three twist dog and the balloon technique we are learning is a called a loop twist.

In the real world there are big dogs, little dogs, long dogs, short dogs, and this is the same in the balloon world. Experiment with proportions and positioning for your perfect puppy.

Top Secret Information –

Using this formula, a dog with a long neck is a giraffe, a little dog with a long uninflated tail is a mouse, a dog with big ears and little legs is a rabbit.

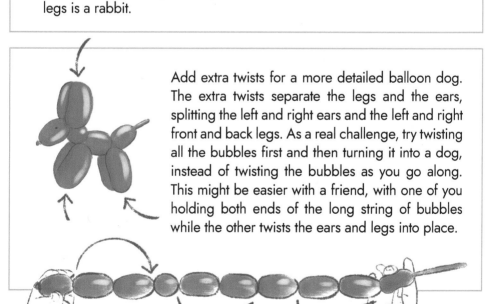

Add extra twists for a more detailed balloon dog. The extra twists separate the legs and the ears, splitting the left and right ears and the left and right front and back legs. As a real challenge, try twisting all the bubbles first and then turning it into a dog, instead of twisting the bubbles as you go along. This might be easier with a friend, with one of you holding both ends of the long string of bubbles while the other twists the ears and legs into place.

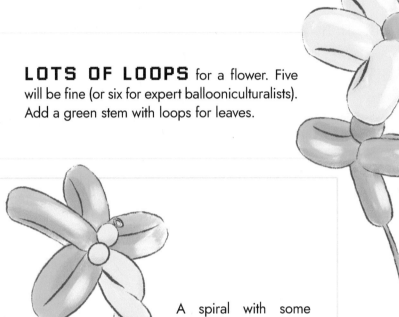

LOTS OF LOOPS for a flower. Five will be fine (or six for expert ballooniculturalists). Add a green stem with loops for leaves.

A spiral with some green loops added — it's a palm tree, (well, at least a rubber plant).

NO LOOPS for a bow and arrow, just inflate a balloon, half full and tie the uninflated end back onto the knot. You might need to add another uninflated balloon to make the string longer. Inflate another balloon for an arrow.

A BIG LOOP around your head and curve over the top for a hat.

Add more balloons for a more extravagant and eye-catching (sometimes literally) hat.

AND FINALLY, The Golden Rules of Balloon Modelling — there are no rules (golden or otherwise). Experiment and improvise (make it up as you go along) and have fun as you unleash the balloon artist... and the scientist,

WITHIN YOU.

*No balloon dogs, big or small, were popped during the creation of this book!